Educating the changing world in the science of colour

Published by the Society of Dyers and Colourists
PO Box 244, Perkin House, 82 Grattan Road,
Bradford, West Yorkshire, BD1 2JB, England
www.sdc.org.uk
www.colour.sdc.org.uk

ISBN 978-0-901956-94-1

Printed by Think Digital Books
53 Farm Road, Weston-super-Mare, Somerset, BS22 8BE

Weaver of Life in colour
and
Malcolm the Weaver
Blackhouse boy (the early years)

This book is dedicated to the memory of my mother and Sharon's grandmother,
Frances Dodds Campbell, who was a tweed cloth mender
and who was my inspiration for life, and my teacher of magical things.
Malcolm Campbell

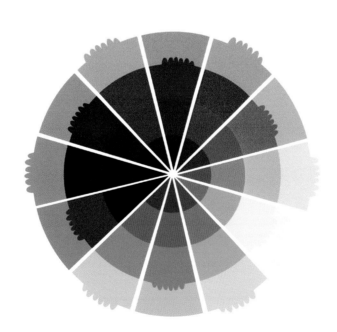

Written by Malcolm Campbell   Illustrated by Sharon Campbell

Malcolm the Weaver
Blackhouse boy (the early years)

Malcolm the weaver weaves dreams, but he didn't always weave dreams, oh no...

When he was a little boy, he had no idea what he wanted to be when he grew up...a policeman, an artist, a spaceman, a spy?
Perhaps even a weaver? But he could not weave... he didn't know how.

His dream was then to learn the many crafts of textiles, colour and weaving.

Malcolm loved being outside. He loved seeing nature, feeling nature, smelling nature and sensing nature. He was always in the open air, in the woods, on the beach, in the hills, playing in the fields or climbing on the rocks.

Malcolm was comfortable and at one with the birds, the flowers, their colours, the animals and the fish.

He was a very happy wee boy, like a little lone wolf.

Whether he was in the sun, out in the rain, blowing in the wind or under the full moon, it did not matter, Oh no no no...

Whatever the weather, Malcolm knew that the whole shebang was exactly the same, just hotter, colder, drier, windier or wetter, depending on the climate.

If things were not quite right, if he didn't feel quite as good as he should, he would think of calm and happiness and begin to feel better again.

He began to realise that there was a magic, that he could change things... change them from bad to good.

Malcolm lived on a beautiful island in Scotland called the Isle of Lewis. He would listen to Roddy the weaver in the thatched Blackhouse cottages which were home to his family and animals...

Shuttle, treadle, weave, pick... Shuttle, treadle, weave, pick...

Weaving more and more cloth, with wool from the Cheviot Sheep, spun into beautiful woollen yarns.

Shuttle
treadle
weave
pick

The yarns were dyed into glorious colours from natures plants and flowers...

Scarlet from privet berries, reddish brown from lichen and moss, orange from brambles, yellow from teazle and fern roots, greens from heather, blue from elderberry, violet from cress and bilberries, magenta from dandelion roots, black from oak bark and lily roots and birch bark made beige. There are so many colours and so many plants, fruit and vegetables that make them.

The handloom weaver wove the amazing coloured yarns into wonderful cloth including herringbones, tartans and dog tooth designs.

Shuttle, treadle, weave, pick... Shuttle, treadle, weave, pick...

The cloth was then washed in the streams to clean it and make it beautiful.

Herringbones

Callanish Tartan

Dog tooth

Suddenly all became clear, Malcolm was so inspired by the wonder of the weaver at work, that he decided he too was going to be a weaver of cloth... to learn the magic of the loom, to spin yarns, tell stories and weave dreams.

Shuttle
treadle
weave
pick

His hopes and wishes would come true...

Bad things would be good, cruel things would be kind, sad things would be happy, wise things, funny things, curious things...

The magic would loom over the whole caboodle.

Weaver of a Life in colour

When he grew up, Malcolm the weaver created all the colours that he wove in to his cloth designs very carefully, to make sure that his patterns were beautiful, and that all the colours were in harmony together.

Nobody wants to see a world without colour, it would be very dull and sad.

Everybody has a favourite colour, and Malcolm the weaver keeps everyone happy with his spectrum of shades, and he tells what his colours mean and how they affect life, moods, happiness, and contentment.

Colour makes a world of difference.

Wonderful colours make you feel wonderfully happy.

A colour shows you what shade it is by its 'hue', a red hue, or a green hue. It lets you see if it is a light colour or a dark colour by its 'value'.

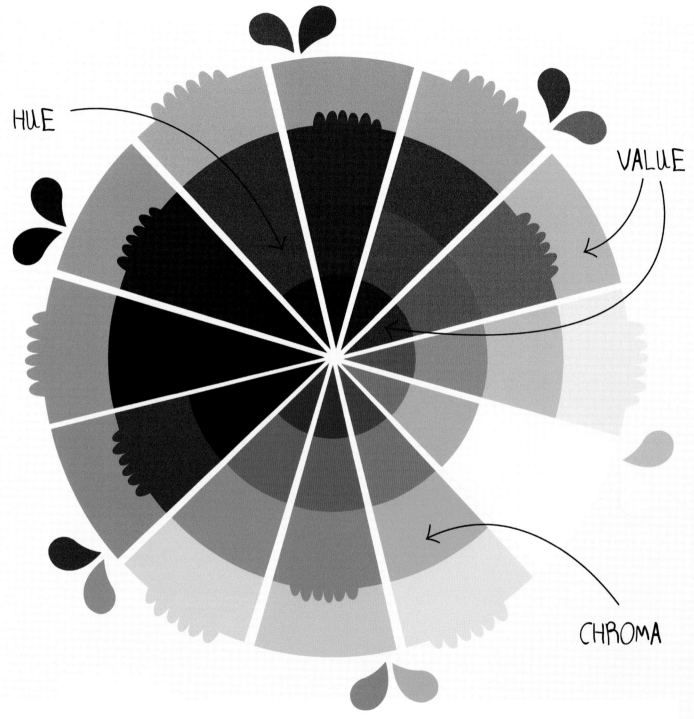

HUE

VALUE

CHROMA

Finally a colour's 'chroma' lets you know if it is a very strong colour, like a scarlet red, or a washed out colour, like a pink.

The same colour will appear differently in different things.

A red brick is different from a red flower, which is different from a red fire engine. They are all red, but they are all different tones of red.

The 3 main colours are called 'PR MA Y C LO RS', because by mixing them, all the other colours can be created.

They are RED, BLUE, and YELLOW

RED and BLUE make PURPLE

BLUE and YELLOW make GREEN

YELLOW and RED make ORANGE

and that's the way it goes.

PURPLE, ORANGE and GREEN are 'SECONDARY COLOURS'...because these are the second colours that are mixed from the 3 main PR MA Y C LO RS.

Then we have BLACK and WHITE, like Tweed the sheep dog. He is a black and white collie dog.

Everything in nature has a colour. Life is woven into many coloured tapestries, with muted colours from the past, bright and vibrant colours for the future and unusual colour combinations from your imagination and in your dreams.

Every bird, flower, plant, fish, animal, person, rock, tree, shell, star, drop of rain, river, sea, mountain, the sun and the moon, even outer space, all have a colour of their very own.

Your eye sees the colour and passes the message of what it has seen to your mind and your brain tells you what the colour is. It is a magical sensation.

See all the colours of life in a natural rainbow, when the sun shines on raindrops, it is a magical thing too.

The colours always run in the same order in a rainbow, from red to orange, yellow, green, blue and then to indigo and violet.

RED IS FOR DANGER, ANGER, LOVE, LEADERSHIP, STRENGTH AND HEAT. STOP SIGNS, ROSES, SANTA, LADYBIRDS AND CHERRIES ARE ALSO RED

HOHOHO

POST HERE PLEASE

ORANGE

ORANGE IS FOR HAPPY, SELLING, AUTUMN, YOUTH AND ACTION. FOXES, PUMPKINS, ORANGES AND FLAMES ARE ALSO ORANGE

YELLOW

YELLOW IS FOR DREAMS, CITRUS, LOYALTY, COWARD AND WISDOM. THE SUN, DAFFODILS, LEMONS, CANARIES AND THE YELLOW SUBMARINE ARE YELLOW.

tweet tweet

GREEN

GO

GREEN IS FOR HEALTH, EARTH, GOOD LUCK, JEALOUSY AND PEACE. FRESHNESS AND GO SIGNS, LIME, GRASS, FROGS AND TREES ARE GREEN.

GOOD LUCK

PURPLE

PURPLE IS FOR MAGIC, NOBILITY, LUXURY, MEDITATION, DREAMS AND WEALTH. GRAPES, AMETHYST JEWELS, VELVET AND PANSIES ARE ALSO PURPLE.

"Abra Cadabra"

When all the colours are mixed up together into one big mess of colour, then the whole caboodle makes...

Malcolm the weaver's dream is to take all the colours of the rainbow and to dye them in wool, then to spin them into a beautiful spangled yarn that would weave into the most glorious cloth in the world.

The magical harris tweed would sparkle in the sunshine and would be used to tailor beautiful clothes that were the finest in the land.

A colourful cloth that would be fit for a king.

From that day forward, the king wore his beautiful clothes made from Tweed. They had been woven on the magic loom in all the wonderful sparkling colours. All the people in the land were happy to see their king so proud and handsome. They knew that he would rule over them well and protect them from harm and evil. Peace, happiness and joy would reign over the whole caboodle.

Birds sang, flowers bloomed, lambs skipped, and the Spring sun shone.

Shuttle, treadle, weave, pick...magic.